The Mini
EASTER
Activity
Book

Robin Currie

Illustrated by Terry Julien

LION PUBLISHING
Oxford • Batavia • Sydney

About This Book

*E*aster is a wonderful time. The spring
weather and the sudden appearance of
animals and flowers make the whole
world seem new and alive.

The Mini Easter Activity Book can help you get
the most out of this special season. And it will
tell you why many people believe Easter is the
greatest celebration of the whole year.

Inside you'll find ideas for decorating your
home or your room, enjoying games and
activities, and discovering lots of creative uses
for Easter eggs. Some of the projects are
especially for Easter. Others will be fun for
any day this spring.

And that's not all. The story of the very first
Easter is also included on pages throughout the
book. Like spring itself, the story of the first
Easter is full of exciting new life, some dark and
stormy weather, and a bright promise of great
things to come.

Happy Easter!

Papier-mâché Baskets

Start getting ready for Easter by making your very own baskets!

1 Blow up a balloon, knot the end, and tie a string to the knot. Wrap the balloon with three layers of newspaper strips dipped in papier-mâché, being careful to leave the knot and string uncovered. (Make your own papier-mâché mix by stirring small amounts of water and flour into a wet paste.)

2 When the papier-mâché is dry, pop the balloon and pull the string to remove it from its shell.

3 Cut off the bottom half of the shell to make the basket. Cut some colored paper into a ⅛ x 10-inch strip and glue it together at the ends. Use this as a base. Cut another piece of paper into 1 x 12-inch strip. Glue the ends to the inside top of the basket, and you've got the handle!

4 Next, paint the basket with poster paint.

5 Fill your basket with artificial grass, then add plastic eggs, Easter cards, or homemade craft like Colored Streamer Sticks.

Joyful Noisemakers

Prepare for a joyful and noisy Easter day with instruments you make yourself.

Fill a clean plastic soda bottle with small pebbles, uncooked rice, jingle bells or dry macaroni. Screw the top on tightly and shake it like a maraca.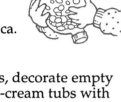

For drums, decorate empty plastic ice-cream tubs with gift wrap or favorite stickers. Turn them upside down and beat on the bottom.

Get eight glass bottles of the same size. Measure ½-inch from the bottom on the first bottle and make a mark. Each of the remaining bottles should have the mark ½-inch higher than the one before. Fill the bottles with water up to the lines, and make chime sounds by tapping them with spoons.

"Hosanna!"

Long ago, God sent his Son, Jesus, into the world to show everyone how much God loved them.

As he grew into a man, many people were happy to hear the things Jesus told them about God. They watched in amazement when he did wonderful things to help people.

Jesus was a Jew, and he lived in Palestine in the Middle East. Near the end of his life on earth, Jesus traveled to the city of Jerusalem to celebrate the Jewish festival called Passover. Outside the city, he told his friends to get a young donkey for him to ride into Jerusalem.

Many people had come to the city for Passover. When they heard that Jesus was coming, they ran to greet him. They laid their coats on the ground in front of Jesus' donkey. They grabbed palm branches and waved them as they shouted, "Hosanna! Praise to God!" They treated Jesus like a king.

Some people, though, did not like Jesus. They did not understand who he was. Some of them were jealous of him. Others were afraid that he might get too powerful. So they made plans to get rid of Jesus.

Colored Streamer Sticks

Greet Easter morning with color and song.

1 Cut four to six 36-inch streamers of crepe paper. These can be all one color or a variety.

2 Wrap one end of each streamer around a stick or an unsharpened pencil. Tape or staple in place.

3 You may wish to make two streamer sticks to wave yourself, or make one for every member of your family to use.

4 Wave your colored streamers while singing Easter songs or to greet the Easter sunrise.

Papier-mâché Egg Surprise

How can you get a surprise from a paper egg? Put one in yourself!

1 Blow up a balloon and knot the end. Wrap a long piece of string around the middle of the balloon, taping one end to the balloon and leaving the other end free.

2 Cover the balloon and string with strips of papier-mâché. Be sure to leave one end of the string uncovered. And leave an opening near the knot so you can remove your balloon.

3 When the papier-mâché is dry, pop the balloon and remove it. Place a small chick or candy eggs inside, and seal the opening with papier-mâché.

4 Paint the egg with bright poster paint. Make sure the string is still exposed.

5 When it is time to open the egg, pull the string. The egg will open in the middle and out will come the surprise!

Jesus' Last Supper

Jesus knew that some important people in the temple at Jerusalem hated him. He knew that going to Jerusalem was dangerous. But he went anyway.

In Jerusalem, Jesus visited the temple and taught people about God. Later, he ate the special Passover meal with his followers.

While they were eating, Jesus held up a loaf of bread. After thanking God for it, he broke it into pieces and shared these with his friends. Jesus told them that his body would be broken like the loaf.

Then Jesus took a cup of wine and, after giving thanks, he passed it to his friends. "Drink, all of you," he told them. And he told them that his blood would be poured out like the wine.

Jesus tried to explain that he was going to die in order to take the punishment for the sins of everyone in the world. He also tried to explain that he would live again. But his friends didn't understand what he meant.

When they had eaten, Jesus and his friends sang together and went outside to a nearby garden.

Coloring Eggs

An egg looks like a hard rock. But when it hatches, a wonderful little chick appears. That is why eggs are a good symbol for Easter. They remind us that new life can come from unexpected places.

1 Ask a grown-up to help you boil some eggs. Let them cool.

2 Buy a package of egg dye and prepare it according to the instructions, or make your own dye using drops of food coloring in bowls of hot water. Use a different bowl or cup for each color.

3 Dunk an egg in the dye only a short time for a pale color. Leave it in longer for a deeper color. Give your eggs a "tie-dyed" look by putting pieces of tape or string around the egg before you dye it. When the egg is dyed, remove the tape or string. Give some eggs two or more colors by dipping different parts of the egg in different colored dyes.

4 After the eggs are dry, even more decorations can be added with stickers and felt pens.

You can eat your colored eggs or use them for games. But you'll need to store them in the refrigerator.

Giving Day

The Thursday before Easter is called Maundy Thursday. "Maundy" comes from a Latin word that means commandment. On the Thursday before he died, Jesus commanded his friends to love one another.

Maundy Thursday can be a special time for letting others know that we care about them. Here are some ideas:

1 Collect cans or newspapers for recycling. Donate any money you earn to local groups that help needy people.

2 When your family buys the food for your Easter dinner, ask if you can pick up extra canned meat and vegetables and packaged desserts. Donate these to a food pantry.

3 Donate pet food to an animal shelter. (Call first to see what kind they like to feed the animals.)

4 Fill a basket with treats and toys. Take it to the children's unit of a hospital to be handed out on Easter morning.

A Friend Who Lied

When Jesus and his friends got to the garden, Jesus went off by himself to pray. It was late at night, and his friends all fell asleep.

Suddenly a crowd of soldiers marched into the garden. They took Jesus away to be put on trial.

Jesus' friend Peter followed them. While Jesus' enemies were accusing him of things he'd never done, Peter waited to find out what would happen.

As Peter waited, a stranger came up to him. "Did you know Jesus?" Peter feared what might happen if he told the truth, so he said, "No." Later, someone else said, "I thought you were Jesus' friend." But Peter said, "No, I'm not."

Near dawn, a third person said, "You are from Galilee, like Jesus is. Surely you know him." Peter was angry and frightened. He shouted, "No! I don't!"

Then a rooster crowed. It was morning. Peter remembered that Jesus had told him, "Before the rooster crows, you will say three times that you don't know me."

Peter was so ashamed that he began to cry.

Chick-in-an-Egg

Remember that the egg is the sign of new life. Make an egg and chick for friends or Easter-time guests.

1 Carefully break an egg in half. Use the insides for cooking and clean the shell completely.

2 Paint the inside and outside of the shell with poster paint or decorate with colored markers.

3 Glue a small, store-bought chick in each of the egg shells.

4 Make enough for each of your friends or guests, or take a basketful of chick-in-an-egg decorations to a retirement home or hospital.

Easter Greetings

Cards you make yourself mean more than store-bought ones to the people you love.

1 Fold a 9 x 12-inch piece of colored paper in half. Starting at the fold, cut out a large oval shape—like a giant Easter egg. Be sure you don't cut all the way through the fold.

2 Decorate the outside of this egg with stickers or felt markers.

3 Open up your decorated card and, on the inside, write an Easter greeting and sign your name.

4 Deliver these to your neighbors, friends, or family.

Jesus Is Put to Death

When Jesus' trial was over, Pilate, the Roman governor, said he was innocent. But Jesus' enemies shouted that he should be put to death. Because he was afraid of the people, Pilate agreed to have Jesus killed.

On Friday afternoon, at around 3 o'clock, Jesus' hands and feet were nailed to a large wooden cross. This was the usual way of putting the worst criminals to death. The cross was stuck into the ground at the top of a lonely hill called "the place of the skull."

After Jesus died, a man named Joseph asked if he could bury Jesus' body in his own tomb. Joseph loved Jesus and wanted to give him a proper burial. He took Jesus' body down from the cross, wrapped it carefully in cloth, and placed it in a tomb.

Then soldiers rolled a heavy stone in front of the doorway and sealed the tomb. A guard stood watch to make sure nobody would try to take Jesus' body away.

"What's So Good About Good Friday?"

*P*alm Sunday (the Sunday before Easter) is called this because crowds of people welcomed Jesus into Jerusalem by waving palm branches. Maundy Thursday reminds us of Jesus' command to love others. But what's so good about Good Friday?

Not much, it might seem. That was the day many people turned against Jesus, the Son of God, and put him to death. According to the Bible, the sky turned black and the earth shook when Jesus died.

Jesus knew this would happen. But he let himself be killed as punishment for the wrong things everyone else had done.

He had told his friends that he would come alive again in three days. Death wasn't strong enough to hold him. And Jesus said that those who believed he was God's Son would come alive again too.

That really *is* good news!

Good Friday Garden

Good Friday is a wonderful time to plant a miniature garden. Soon beautiful flowers will bloom from your seeds, reminding you of the new life that bloomed on the first Easter morning.

1 Find a small plastic flower pot or a yogurt or cottage-cheese cup. If there aren't any holes in the bottom, make some with a knife or scissors. Ask an adult if you need help.

 2 Put small pebbles over the bottom of the pot and fill it with potting soil. Put the pot on a saucer, in case water or soil spills out the holes.

3 Buy packets of flower or herb seeds at a local gardening store. Plant the seeds according to the instructions.

4 As your plants grow, keep them watered and see that they get enough sun. Later, they can be transplanted into a garden or put into separate pots to give to friends.

Floating Easter Lights

This pretty decoration can be the centerpiece for your Easter dinner table. It can be used again for birthdays or other special times. You can light the candles after dark for a peaceful effect.

1 Collect 10-12 smooth stones.

2 Paint them with poster paint and coat them with clear polyurethane. They may look like colored eggs!

3 When they are completely dry, put them in a glass bowl and fill the bowl with water.

4 Make your own floating candles by placing a short, wide candle on the upside-down lid of a small jar. You may also buy small candles that are made to float on water.

Once you have lit them, sit back and enjoy the flickering light as your candles dance.

Hot Cross Buns

These delicious spicy buns marked with a cross are a traditional Good Friday treat.

You will need the following:

2 cups flour
4 tablespoons butter or margarine
2 tablespoons sugar
1 cup warm milk
1 envelope yeast
1 small egg, beaten
1/2 cup raisins
1/4 cup mixed lemon/orange peel
pinch of salt
pinch of mixed spice or pumpkin spice
a plastic bag
a spoonful of corn oil

1 Sift flour, salt and spice into a large bowl.

2 Dissolve the butter and sugar in the warm milk, and add the yeast. Leave for 3 minutes, stir once, then mix in a small, beaten egg.

3 Pour the liquid into the flour and beat until smooth.

4 Move the dough onto a floured surface and knead in the raisins and mixed peel. Knead for 5 minutes, until the dough is smooth and shiny.

5 Put the oil inside the plastic bag and scrunch it up to grease the inside. Place dough in the bag and put it in a warm place to rise.

6 When the dough has doubled in size, remove it and thump all the air out of it. When it's back to its original size, put it in the greased bag and leave it to rise again for half an hour in a warm place.

7 Remove the dough and shape it into four round buns. Cut a cross on the top of each with the back of a knife.

8 Leave the buns on a greased cookie sheet for about 20 minutes. Then, bake them in the oven at 450 degrees for 15-20 minutes.

The buns bake best in a steamy oven, so put a pan of water on the bottom of the oven.

Always ask for help when putting the buns into the oven and taking them out.

Women Go to the Tomb

Very early on the Sunday after Jesus died, three women friends of Jesus were walking toward the garden where his tomb was. They wanted to visit the tomb and put sweet-smelling spices on Jesus' body to help preserve it.

As they walked, one woman said, "There was a large stone in front of the tomb."

Another said, "Who will move it away so we can get into the tomb?"

But when the women arrived at the garden, they were amazed at what they saw. The enormous stone was rolled away from the tomb. The tomb was empty!

One of the women, named Mary, ran back to town to tell Jesus' friends. When she found his friends Peter and John, she said, "Someone has taken Jesus out of the tomb, and we don't know where they've put him!"

Rolling Stone Flip Book

M*ake a flip book that shows how the stone rolled away from the front of the tomb.*

1 Collect or cut 25 sheets of 3 x 5-inch paper. Staple together one side of the papers to form a booklet.

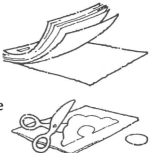

2 Cut a cave shape out of thick card. Next, cut a stone shape big enough to go over the opening of the cave.

3 On the last few pages in the booklet trace the cave with the stone covering the opening. On the next page or two, trace the cave with the stone moved just slightly out of the way. Keep changing the position of the stone slightly in each picture until by picture 25 (at the front of your flip book) the stone is completely away from the cave.

4 Flip the pages to see the stone "move."

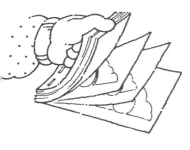

Easter Dinner Decorations

Whether you're having a large gathering of friends or just family, place mats and place cards help to make your Easter meals special.

1 Use a 3 x 5-inch index card to make a place card for each guest you're expecting. Use 9 x 12-inch sheets of colored paper for place mats.

2 To make place cards, fold the index cards in half lengthwise. Print the name of the person on the front, and decorate with crayons or stickers. If you like, add your own special greeting to the inside.

3 To make place mats, draw an Easter picture on one side of each piece of paper. Cover that side with clear self-adhesive paper.

4 For a different look, fold the colored paper in half, then in half again. Cut a pattern along the edges. When you unfold the paper, you'll have a decorative place mat.

No-Cook Easter Candy

These easy-to-make egg-shaped treats make a perfect dessert for an Easter meal.

Gather the following ingredients:

8 oz powdered sugar
1 egg
flavoring (pick your favorite!) and food coloring

1 Sift the sugar into a bowl.

2 Separate the white from the yolk of the egg. Beat the egg white until it's stiff.

For strawberry eggs, add three drops of strawberry flavoring and three drops of red food coloring to the egg white. For peppermint eggs, add peppermint flavor. Try other flavors and colors.

3 Slowly fold the flavored egg white into the sugar.

4 Stir the mixture with a table knife until well blended.

5 Roll into small egg shapes and set them on a plate lightly covered with powdered sugar.

Lights for Easter

Jesus said that he was the light of the world, a light pointing to the goodness and life that come from God. Easter is a good time to celebrate the light that Jesus brought to the world.

1 Remove the labels from 15-20 large, green, plastic soda bottles. Carefully cut off the tops using scissors or a craft knife. (You may want to ask an adult to help you.)

2 Fill each bottle ⅓ full of sand and stand a candle in it.

3 Line your front walk with these Easter lights, then light them.

4 You may wish to use the lights for a message, such as "Jesus Is Alive." Use masking tape to form a letter on each bottle. Stand the bottles on a porch or in a window. When you light the candles, your message can be seen from the street.

Easter Banners

In parades and in churches, banners add a colorful, festive touch to celebrations. Make your own banners to announce Easter's arrival.

1 Cut a large rectangle from colored paper or felt. (The bigger the better!) Using glue or staples, attach one end of the paper or felt to a wooden rod.

2 Choose a special Easter scene—one you draw yourself, or one cut out of a magazine—and decide where you'll place it on your banner.

3 Draw or glue the scene onto your banner.

4 Add fabric trim, glitter, tassels or small bells to your banner.

5 During Easter, proudly display your banner on a door or in your room.

Butterflies for Easter!

A cocoon seems dry and dead, but in time a beautiful new butterfly will come out. This reminds us of how Jesus came alive again at Easter.

 1 Draw a large butterfly shape on plain 9 x 12-inch paper. Cut this out and use it as a pattern.

2 Get two sheets of 9 x 12-inch brown paper and two sheets of 9 x 12-inch yellow paper. Trace your pattern onto each sheet, then cut out the shapes.

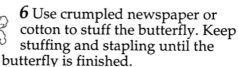 **3** Cut holes and squiggles out of the yellow butterflies.

4 Glue each yellow butterfly onto a brown one.

5 With the brown sides together, staple halfway around the outside edge of the butterflies.

6 Use crumpled newspaper or cotton to stuff the butterfly. Keep stuffing and stapling until the butterfly is finished.

7 Use string or thread to hang your butterfly where everyone will see it.

 Repeat steps 1-7 for a whole flock of beautiful butterflies!

Stone Rolling Game

*I*f lots of friends and family gather at Easter time, here's a game that everyone will enjoy.

1 Collect 6-8 smooth stones.

2 Form relay teams of 2-6 people. Give each team a stone.

3 Decide how the stones will be rolled. Can people use their hands? Only their feet? Only a stick or spoon?

4 Each player must roll the stone from the starting line to a set point and back again to the next player in line. The first team to finish wins.

Sometimes people play this game using hard-boiled eggs instead of stones. Why not see which you like better?

Peter and John at the Tomb

Mary told her friends Peter and John that Jesus' tomb was open, and his body was gone. When they heard the news, Peter and John ran to see for themselves.

Peter ran fast but John ran faster. When they both came to the garden, they peered into the open tomb. The sheets that had been around Jesus' body were still there. The cloth that had been laid over Jesus' face was there, neatly folded nearby. But Jesus was nowhere to be seen.

Peter and John did not know what to think. Did someone take Jesus' body away?

Or was it possible that Jesus really was alive?

Egg Games

*E*aster is a day for eggs. These games can be played with hard-boiled eggs. Or be daring and try them with uncooked eggs!

Roll eggs downhill to see whose gets to the bottom first. Or, in a flat area, have people race to push their eggs to a finish line without breaking them.

Divide into relay race teams, and give each person a spoon. Each player must carry the egg to a set point and back, and pass it off to the next person's spoon without touching the egg. If the egg falls, it must be replaced before the player races on. The first team to finish wins.

Stand in a circle and have one egg for every three players. Give one egg a special color or marking. Play music while the eggs are passed around the circle. When the music stops, the one holding the special egg is out. Continue until only one person is left.

Company for Easter Breakfast

Last minute touches will make your Easter breakfast more fun—and this is a day to laugh and be joyful!

1 Select one hard-boiled egg for each family member. The eggs can be plain or already colored.

2 Use felt markers to draw eyes, nose, and mouth on each egg.

3 Glue on paper hair or hats.

4 Cut a 1 x 2½-inch strip of colored paper for each egg. Join the ends with tape, so you have small circular "display stands." Set a stand in front of each plate on the table, and put an egg in each one.

Easter Tree Mobile

1 Cut large egg shapes from colored paper. Decorate them with felt markers and glitter. Cut a cross, an angel, butterflies, or flowers from paper, and color them.

2 Punch holes in the tops of your cut-out shapes and run various lengths of thread through them.

3 Next, cut a large "T" from heavy cardboard. Punch or cut holes along the bottom of the "T" for hanging all your shapes.

4 For an extra special touch, hang plastic eggs, bells, and crepe-paper streamers along with your paper shapes.

Hang your mobile high, so all your decorations can dangle freely in the air.

Mary Meets the Gardener

After Peter and John had seen the empty tomb, they went back to tell Jesus' friends. The only one left in the garden was Mary. She wanted to know who had taken Jesus' body and where they put it. She wondered why this terrible thing had happened. Mary started to cry.

As Mary was crying, two angels appeared in the tomb where Jesus' body had been. They said, "Why are you crying?"

"They have taken Jesus away," Mary said, "and I don't know where they've put him." Then she turned around and saw a stranger standing behind her. Thinking he was the gardener, Mary said to him, "Sir, if you've taken Jesus away, please tell me where you have put him and I will go get him."

Then the man said only one word: "Mary."

Suddenly Mary recognized him. It was Jesus himself! He was alive! Mary cried out with joy and ran to tell Jesus' friends the wonderful news.

Your Own Easter Tree

There is something wonderful about bringing new, green life into the house at Easter time. Like Easter itself, buds and flowers in springtime can remind us of God's promise of new life.

1 Cut several branches from a leafy or flowering bush, such as forsythia. Stand the branches in a large vase of water.

2 Cut egg shapes out of paper and decorate with stickers or felt markers. You may also cut some traditional symbols for Jesus, such as a fish or a cross. Decorate these with glitter.

3 Hang your decorations from the branches you've gathered.

Paschal Candle

*M*any churches light a large candle on Easter to celebrate Jesus' coming alive and to remember that he called himself the light of the world. Paschal is an old word meaning "Passover" or "Easter."

1 Choose a tall, wide candle that will not burn too quickly. Set it in a candle stand or on a fire-proof dish.

2 Light the candle on Easter day. You might sing an Easter hymn or shout "Jesus is alive!"

3 Some churches continue to light the candle each day for the next 50 days, when the Easter season ends. Burning your own candle for 50 days after Easter can help you keep the spirit of Easter alive for more than just a day.

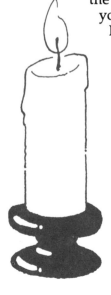

4 After the 50th day, save the candle to burn on birthdays, anniversaries and other meaningful occasions in your home. It's a good way to remember that Jesus can bring his light and love to every celebration.

Garden Diorama

*I*magine you were in the garden where Jesus rose from the dead. What might you have seen when the sun rose on Easter morning? Who would have been there? Now make a three-dimensional model of your idea.

1 Collect some soil, and pieces of moss, stones, twigs, and tiny flowers. Use the lid of a shoe box (turned upside down) for your base.

2 Form a cave out of soil and moss and stones.

3 Use twigs to make trees and bushes. Use colored paper to cut out angels and the people who were in the garden.

4 Surround your "garden" with pieces of moss for grass and tiny flowers.

Make an Easter Hat

*H*ats are making a comeback—
especially at Easter! Easter bonnets have
been enjoyed for years. And special hats
for Easter can make everyone smile.

1 For a base you can use
an old hat, stocking cap,
plastic bowl, or shoe box.

2 Use cut-out pictures from magazines or draw
your own decorations.

3 Glue or stitch your
decorations to the hat.
Add crepe-paper
streamers or ribbons.

4 Attach ribbons or an elastic band to each side
of your hat. Slip or tie these under your chin so
the hat stays on.

Seeing Is Believing

When Jesus' closest friends heard about the empty tomb, they did not know what to think. Peter and John said Jesus' body was gone. Now Mary said she saw Jesus alive and that she talked with him. Jesus' friends met in a room to talk about all that was happening.

While they talked, suddenly Jesus stood there among them. He said, "Peace be with you."

Jesus' friends were so happy they could not believe their eyes. But Jesus showed them the wounds on his hands and feet where he had been nailed to the cross. Then the disciples knew it was the same Jesus who had died and been buried.

Then Jesus asked for something to eat. His friends gave him some fish and he ate it. That was how he showed the disciples he was really alive.

Everlasting Eggs

*H*ard-boiled eggs should be eaten soon after Easter, but you can make and decorate eggs that will last for months—or years. Ask a grown-up to help with this project. Make it a family activity.

1 Hold a raw egg over a mixing bowl. Make a hole in one end with a large needle.

2 Make a hole in the other end and gently move the needle around until the hole is about ½-inch wide. Blow gently through the smaller hole and the insides of the egg will come out the other end. Carefully rinse out the egg with warm water.

3 Dye or decorate the shell using paint, markers, glitter—whatever you want. For extra strength, coat the shell with clear polyurethane.

4 After Easter, wrap the eggs up and carefully put them away. You can enjoy these artful eggs each Easter for a long time.

Bursts of Color

Easter Sunday is a time for dressing up in bright new clothes. You can wear Easter's bright colors on other days too. Ask an adult to help you with this activity.

1 This is a good outdoor project. Prepare clothing dye, as many colors as you want, in buckets, according to the directions on the package. (You may want to wear rubber gloves, even if the package doesn't mention them.)

2 Select a light-colored cloth or an old white T-shirt. Gather the fabric at different places and tie it tightly with a rubber band or string.

3 Dip the tied parts of the fabric into the dye for 2-3 minutes. If you want more than one color, simply dip different tied-off parts into different colors.

4 Rinse the fabric in plain water. Take off the rubber bands or strings and see the explosion of color.

Friends on the Road

*L*ater on that first Easter, two friends were walking from Jerusalem to a town called Emmaus.

As they walked, Jesus appeared beside them. But they did not recognize him. In fact when Jesus asked what they were talking about, they thought he must be the only one in Jerusalem who hadn't heard the incredible news!

The men explained to the stranger what Jesus' followers had told them. They still did not know that this stranger was Jesus himself.

When they came to an inn, the friends invited Jesus to eat with them. Jesus said a prayer as they began to eat. The men suddenly realized who Jesus was. Just as suddenly, Jesus disappeared.

The men ran back to Jerusalem with wonderful news of their own. They had seen Jesus. He was alive!

The Easter Bunny

Where does the Easter Bunny come from?

The story really goes back to the Easter Hare. A hare is a relative of the rabbit, with longer ears, large hind feet, and long legs—perfect for jumping.

In the early years of Easter celebrations, hares were compared with Jesus. They were known for being gentle. They have no burrow or home (Jesus wandered through the countryside, and he said that he had no home in this world). And they symbolize the new life that comes every spring and during Easter.

Nowadays, the once-kingly hare is usually pictured as a cute little bunny that delivers eggs. Most people don't think of it as having any religious meaning or history at all.

You can help change that. This year, as you see pictures and cards with the Easter Bunny on them, remember the story of the Son of God who rose from the dead and brings new life.

Secret Message Spinner

First, the angels knew. Then Jesus' friends heard. Now millions of people know: Jesus is alive!

1 Cut a circle 3 inches in diameter from heavy cardboard. Punch two holes across from each other, about ½-inch from the outside of the circle.

2 Write "Jesus is" with a bright marker on the top half of one side, placing all the letters above the holes.

3 Turn the circle over, so the first words you wrote are upside down and face-down. Write "alive!" above the center holes.

4 Loop a rubber band through each hole. Slip your index fingers through the bands. Wind the circle until the bands are twisted. Spread your hands apart to see the message.

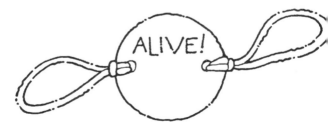

Pressed Flower Bookmarks

Collect spring flowers and make them last throughout the year.

1 Gather tiny wildflowers and colorful leaves. Be sure it's all right to pick flowers before you begin.

2 Press the flowers and leaves in an old phone book. Skip about 10 pages between each flower. Stack several heavy books on top of the phone book.

3 Check the flowers after a week. Some can take as long as a month to dry completely.

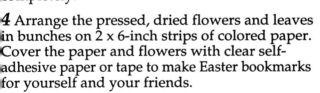

4 Arrange the pressed, dried flowers and leaves in bunches on 2 x 6-inch strips of colored paper. Cover the paper and flowers with clear self-adhesive paper or tape to make Easter bookmarks for yourself and your friends.

Pocketful of Flowers

This cheerful pocket of flowers can brighten your room all year long.

1 Cut a strip of colored paper 5 x 9 inches.

2 Round off the corners of one end of the paper strip and punch a hole in that end.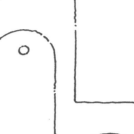

3 Fold the other end up to form a 3-inch flap. Staple or glue the sides of the flap to make a pocket.

4 Put dried flowers and leaves in the pocket. Tie a bow through the hole in the top and proudly hang it in your room.

Bread Bag Kite

Feel like running? Or is there a good breeze? Spring is the perfect time of year to enjoy the sun and wind by flying this simple-to-make kite.

1 Cut three 2-inch-wide loops from the open end of an empty, plastic bread bag.

2 Cut open the loops and knot them together to form a long tail for your kite. Tape this tail to the closed end of the bread bag.

3 Make a small hole an inch back from the open end of the bag. Tie on a long piece of string for sailing the kite in the breeze. Or, if you want to run and let the kite sail out behind you, tie on a shorter string and slip it on your wrist.

Easter Wreath

Wreaths brighten any door and reflect the mood of the people who live there. Make a joyful wreath for this time of year

1 Use a Styrofoam wreath base. Cut out enough colored paper leaves to cover the base.

2 Pin the leaves to the base, overlapping them so no Styrofoam shows.

3 On top of the wreath, glue or pin pompom chicks, artificial flowers plastic eggs and other decorations. (Maybe some of these are left over from centerpieces or old Easter baskets.)

4 Add a bow and ribbons or crepe-paper streamers in bright colors. Attach a loop of picture-hanging wire to the back and hook the wreath over a nail.

Breakfast with Jesus

*E*arly one morning, while Jesus' friends were fishing on a lake, Jesus appeared on the shore. The fishermen did not know it was Jesus. He called to them, "Did you catch any fish?"

When the men said no, Jesus said, "Try putting your nets on the right side of the boat instead of the left."

When Jesus' friends did this, they caught more fish than they could count. Then they recognized Jesus on the shore. When they pulled their boats onto the beach, Peter ran to meet Jesus.

Peter and Jesus had a long talk together. Peter remembered the night he said he didn't know Jesus, and he felt ashamed. But Jesus loved Peter. He wasn't angry with him. In fact, Jesus gave Peter a special job. Peter was to look after Jesus' friends and followers.

Read It for Yourself

You can read the whole story of the first Easter for yourself in the Bible.

The first four books in the New Testament are Matthew, Mark, Luke and John. The Easter story appears in Matthew, chapters 26-28; Mark chapters 14-16; Luke, chapters 22-24; and John, chapters 18-21.

Each of these four books tells about Jesus, what he taught, why he died and how he came to life again.

Jesus came to offer every one of us a whole new life, with God himself as our friend. That's the best Easter present of all!

Copyright © 1993 Lion Publishing

Published by
Lion Publishing
1705 Hubbard Avenue, Batavia, IL 60510, USA
ISBN 0 7459 2149 3

The recipe for Hot Cross Buns is taken from *The Easter Activity Book* by Susan Vesey, copyright © 1987 by Lion Publishing. Used by permission.

The recipe for No-Cook Easter Candy is adapted from *The Mini Christmas Activity Book* by Susan Vesey and Meryl Doney, copyright © 1990 by Lion Publishing. Used by permission.

Cover illustration: Amelia Rosato
Interior illustrations: Terry Julien

Printed and bound in the United States